IN THE
STREET

This I-SPY book belongs
to:_____

Introduction

Most of us live in towns and cities and we often take the roads and streets for granted. In every street there is something interesting – there are always people working, bus stops, lamps, shops, street notices, signs, vehicles and much, much more. Most of us take a journey that involves walking or driving along a street, it could be to school or to work and more often than not we scarcely look around us. But even the most seemingly humdrum of workaday streets is full of interest if you keep your I-Spy eyes open.

The things that you can spot on country roads will be different to what you can see in the towns and cities. It may be quite easy to see a horse and rider or village green in the countryside but quite difficult to find a grand town hall or multi-story car-park. There will be a lot more traffic in the towns and cities in the form of buses, taxis, cars and bicycles. Or some areas may be designated for pedestrians only. There are always many fascinating things to do and see.

Take your I-Spy In the Street with you when you visit family or friends, or go on holiday and seek out particular places of interest. We have given you plenty of examples, but just look around you, about you, above your head and down to your feet, you'll be surprised what is around you!!

How to use your I-SPY book

s you work through this book, you will notice that the subjects are arranged in groups which are related to the kinds of places where you are likely to find things. You need 1000 points to send off for your I-Spy certificate (see page 64) but that is not too difficult because there are masses of points in every book. As you make each I-Spy, write your score in the box and, where there is a question, double your score if you can answer it. Check your answer against the correct one on page 63.

I-SPY TITLES AVAILABLE:

TRAFFIC LIGHTS

Traffic lights were invented in 1868 and were originally powered by gas. Today, they are controlled by computers and regulate traffic on roads all over the world.

I-SPY points: 5

Date: _____

RAILINGS

Railings are positioned near pedestrian crossings to stop people walking off the kerb and to channel them to the safest point to cross the road.

I-SPY points: 5

Date: _____

TACTILE PAVING

The raised pimples on the ground near a pedestrian crossing are known as 'tactile paving'. It warns people with poor eyesight that they are near the kerb.

I-SPY points: 5

Date: _____

PELICAN CROSSING

A pelican crossing has a push button to control the traffic lights. When it is safe to cross, the green man signs flashes and a bleep alarm sounds.

What does pelican stand for?

I-SPY points: 5
Double with answer

Date: _____

SPEED BUMP

Where cars move more slowly, there are fewer traffic jams and fewer serious accidents. Speed bumps have been installed in streets in many towns, particularly close to schools to slow cars down.

I-SPY points: 5

Date: _____

ZIG-ZAG LINE

White zig-zag lines on the road warn motorists not to park or overtake near a pelican crossing. They are there to ensure better visability around pelican and zebra crossings.

I-SPY points: 5

Date: _____

BELISHA BEACON

Belisha beacons are orange flashing lights on top of black and white striped poles. They warn motorists that a pedestrian crossing is ahead.

Who gave his name to these lights?

I-SPY points: 10

Double with answer

Date: _____

AUTOMATIC BOLLARDS

Bollards are permanently up in position and do not allow normal traffic to pass. Buses have an sensor that automatically transmits to the bollard, lowering it, allowing the bus to pass. Once through the bollard raises itself again.

I-SPY points: 20

Date: _____

BOLLARDS

These white and yellow bollards light up at night to warn drivers that there is an obstacle or a crossing ahead.

I-SPY points: 5

Date: _____

LOLLIPOP LADY

Lollipop ladies or men often help children to cross the road near schools. The long tall sign (which is shaped like a giant lollipop) is bright yellow and orange so that it stands out even on foggy days.

I-SPY points: 10

Date:_____

ZEBRA CROSSING

Zebra crossings consist of black and white stripes on the road. Drivers MUST stop to give way to pedestrians. Some zebra crossing have a look left/look right indicator painted on the road.

-SPY points: 10

)ate:_____

MANHOLE COVER

These circular metal lids are called manhole covers and can be lifted up to give workmen access to the drains and sewers that run underneath the road.

I-SPY points: 10

Date: _____

DRAIN

When it rains, the water runs through the metal grilles and down into the drains. Without them, the road would flood!

I-SPY points: 10

Date: _____

POT HOLE

Pot holes like this are often caused by rain and frost, which make the road surface crack open. These are particularly dangerous to motorcyclists and cyclists.

I-SPY points: 10

Date: _____

COBBLED STREET

Roads were covered by cobbles like these in Victorian times. They can be very slippy in the wet, so be careful.

I-SPY points: 15

Date: _____

TRAFFIC CALMING

In built up areas, around houses or shops, some roads may be made narrower to force cars to slow down and make the street safer for pedestrians.

I-SPY points: 15

Date: _____

ROAD WORKS

Your house is probably kept warm by gas or electricity, which comes from pipes and cables under the ground. The water in your taps also comes from the main pipe in the road.

I-SPY points: 10

Date: _____

DOUBLE YELLOW LINES

You will see a variety of painted lines on many busy streets. Yellow lines warn drivers not to park on the road during the times indicated on a nearby time sign.

I-SPY points: 5

Date: _____

DOUBLE RED LINES

Some busy major routes, in urban areas have double red lines, which mean that no-one can stop their vehicle at any time of the day or night. In this way, traffic can keep moving without stationary vehicles causing traffic jams.

I-SPY points: 15

Date: _____

WEATHER VANE

You may find a weather vane attached to the highest part of a building. These metal structures indicate the direction of the wind. There are many different interesting shapes of weather vanes.

I-SPY points: 15

Date:

SPEED CAMERA

Speed cameras detect vehicles that are going too fast. The camera takes an image of the moving vehicle and determines its speed. A fine may be issued to the driver.

I-SPY points: 10

Date:

SATELLITE DISH

Satellite dishes are mostly white, but try to spot some of the black mesh style, which blends in to the background.

I-SPY points: 5 for white, 10 for black

Date: _____

TV AERIAL

Traditional aerials are spikey and tend to be located on the side of tall chimneys.

I-SPY points: 10

Date: _____

CCTV

CCTV cameras are often positioned high up on the side of buildings and record all the activit in the street below.

What does CCTV stand for?

I-SPY points: 15
Double with answer

Date: _____

TELEGRAPH WIRES

Wooden telegraph poles carry telephone wires between properties. Look out for flocks of birds perched on them! Many telephone wires now run underground.

I-SPY points: 10

Date: _____

CHIMNEYS

Older buildings are sometimes decorated with stone carvings. Look up and see how many different styles of chimney you can see.

I-SPY points: 10 for each style

Date: _____

BLUE PLAQUE

These blue plaques are put on to houses where someone famous once lived. You will find plaques for all sorts of people, from sports to politicians, authors to musicians.

I-SPY points: 10 for each one spotted

Date: _____

15

SCAFFOLDING

Scaffolding covers buildings that are under construction or renovation. They make it easier and safer for work to be done high up.

I-SPY points: 10

Date:

CRANE

Tall, skeletal cranes that tower over houses and buildings are use on building sites to move heavy loads.

I-SPY points: 10

Date:

CRANE SUPPORT

Large cranes need additional support feet to spread the heavy load above them and give them stability.

I-SPY points: 15

Date:

STREET LIGHTS

Street lights are operated with a light-sensitive timer, so they switch on automatically at dusk.

I-SPY points: 10
Double points for
old-style street lights

Date: _____

ADVERTISING LIGHTS

Illuminated advertising signs brighten up a dull evening!

I-SPY points: 15

Date: _____

GUTTERING

Gutters carry rainwater away from the roof of buildings and down into the drains. Old ones are generally made from cast iron and can be very decorative.

I-SPY points: 15

Date: _____

ROOFS

Roofs can be flat or pointed. Some have red tiles, others are covered in grey slate. If you can look down on a street from a high window, look at the jagged outline of many different-shaped buildings with all sorts of different colours.

I-SPY points: 10

Date: _____

Traffic jams are almost unavoidable in big cities. If you're stuck in one, look out for some of the subjects in this book! You're bound to go past a bus stop or a railway station.

TRAFFIC JAM

If you get stuck in a traffic jam, see what you can spy from the car window!

I-SPY points: 10

Date: _____

BUS STOP

You are bound to find a bus stop in a street near you...

I-SPY points: 5

Date: _____

OUT OF ORDER BUS STOP

...but sometimes the bus stop may have to be taken out of service. This can happen if road works are being carried out.

I-SPY points: 25

Date: _____

HOPPER BUS

Single-decker 'hoppers' are more usual on rural routes.

I-SPY points: 10

Date: _____

DOUBLE DECKER BUS

Double-decker buses are more common in towns and cities.

I-SPY points: 5

Date: _____

BENDY BUS

Bendy buses are seen in some city centres and at airports and have replaced double-deckers.

I-SPY points: 20

Date: _____

TRAMS

Trams run on rails through some city streets. Be careful to look both ways when you cross tram lines.

I-SPY points: 20

Date: _____

TAXIS

Taxis are given their own lane in busy city streets...

I-SPY points: 5
Double points for any colour other than black

Date: _____

CYCLIST

...some cyclists are also given their own lanes on busy routes.

I-SPY points: 5

Date: _____

FLAT TYRE

If you get a flat tyre, you'll have to stop – wherever you are!

I-SPY points: 20

Date: _____

SOFT TOP

With the roof rolled back a ride
in a convertible car is fun on a
summer's day.

I-SPY points: 15

Date: _____

4 X 4 VEHICLE

Large four-wheel drive vehicles
are easy to spot as they are higher
than other cars.

I-SPY points: 15

Date: _____

RAILWAY STATION

There are more than 2,400 stations on the National Railways network, ranging in size from great mainline terminals in cities, to small rural stations in the middle of the countryside.

I-SPY points: 10

Date:

LEVEL CROSSING

Barriers at level crossings swing across to block the road when a train passes through. Be careful at all level crossings.

I-SPY points: 15

Date:

CAR PARK

Car parks are dotted around towns and cities. They can vary from large multi storey buildings to small urban spaces.

I-SPY points: 10 for a multi storey, 5 points for any other type

Date: _____

TICKET MACHINE

Don't forget to pay for a ticket from the machine!

I-SPY points: 10

Date: _____

PARKING METER

You can park right next to a parking meter and put money in the slot.

I-SPY points: 10

Date: _____

PARKING TICKET

Oh dear! This driver is in for a nasty shock. If you fail to display the correct parking ticket, or exceed your time, it is likely that a parking ticket will be issued...

I-SPY points: 20

Date:_____

CAR BEING TOWED AWAY

I-SPY points: 25

Date:_____

...and it is possible that the car could be clamped and taken away, which will be more expensive.

Emergency vehicles have fluorescent paintwork and blue flashing lights that make them easy to spot. And if the siren is on, you'll hear them coming!

POLICE CAR
I-SPY points: 10

Date:

AMBULANCE
I-SPY points: 10

Date:

FIRE ENGINE
I-SPY points: 20

Date:

GLASS CARRIER

Glazier vans have special fittings to carry big panes of glass.

I-SPY points: 20

Date: _____

REFUSE LORRY

Bin lorries have special lifts on the back to empty the bins into the interior.

I-SPY points: 10

Date: _____

SECURITY VAN

Security vans, which carry money to banks, are made of toughened steel and glass to deter thieves.

I-SPY points: 20

Date: _____

REMOVAL VAN

These lorries have huge bodies to enable them to carry the maximum amount of furniture.

I-SPY points: 20

Date: _____

CEMENT MIXER

Watch cement mixers carefully, and you will see that the drum rotates slowly so the cement inside doesn't set.

I-SPY points: 15

Date: _____

POSTAL VAN

Postmen in rural areas often have to cover a large area and need a small van to get around.

I-SPY points: 10

Date: _____

RECOVERY VEHICLE

If your car breaks down and can't be repaired at the road side, it is likely that one of these special trucks will be sent out to take it to a local garage.

I-SPY points: 15

Date: _____

CAR TRANSPORTER

Car transporters can carry up to 10 vehicles at a time, and are specially designed to carry as many cars as possible.

I-SPY points: 15

Date: _____

CHERRY PICKER

Cherry pickers are small, mobile cranes, often used to repair street lighting and give access where height is required, but definitely not to pick cherries!

I-SPY points: 15

Date: _____

UNDERGROUND SIGN

You will only see this sign in London, for the Underground system, way below your feet.

I-SPY points: 5

Date: _____

MOBILE LIBRARY

These specially adapted trucks ta[...] a selection of books to the street[...] and give access to people living i[...] remote areas or those who cann[...] easily get to a normal library.

I-SPY points: 20

Date: _____

WOODEN FOOTPATH SIGN

Country signs are often made from wood, rather than metal and can be more in keeping with the surroundings.

I-SPY points: 10

Date:

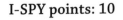

VILLAGE GREEN

The centre of many villages is the green, usually near a crossroads or junction.

I-SPY points: 15

Date:

33

HALF-TIMBERED HOUSE

One way to spot a very old house is to look out for the timbers or wooden frame, which is usually brown or black. These timbers are often anything but straight!

I-SPY points: 15

Date: _____

THATCH HOUSE

Thatched cottages have roofs made of reeds, straw or rushes. There are more thatched roofs in the United Kingdom than any other European country.

I-SPY points: 20

Date: _____

The Boot

PUB SIGN

Look out for interesting pub names and unusual pub signs.

What is the most unusual name you found: ....

I-SPY points: 5

Date: _____

CHURCH

Country churches are among the oldest buildings in the country and are many different styles, dependant on when they were built.

-SPY points: 10

ate: _____

SCHOOL

Village schools often incorporate several different styles of building from Victorian to modern.

I-SPY points: 15

Date: _____

VILLAGE HALL

The centre of the village community is usually the village hall, with a notice board to advertise what's going on.

I-SPY points: 15

Date: _____

HORSES ON STREET

potting a horse on the street in
n urban environment is unusual.
More common would be to find
ne on country lane – the perfect
lace to go for a ride.

I-SPY points: 20

Double points for a horse in an urban street

Date: _____

VILLAGE FAIR

Village fairs are lots of fun,
especially in the summer.

I-SPY points: 15

Date: _____

POST OFFICE

Modern post office signs are oval shaped and are always red. In some villages, they are the centre of the community.

I-SPY points: 5

Date: _____

SCHOOL SIGN

A school sign warms motorists to slow down, as children are likely t be nearby.

I-SPY points: 10

Date: _____

Traffic signs enforce speed limits and warn motorists and pedestrians of hazards ahead

MAXIMUM SPEED
I-SPY points: 5

Date: _____

CYCLE LANE
I-SPY points: 10

Date: _____

ROUNDABOUT
I-SPY points: 5

Date: _____

PEDESTRIAN ZONE

A pedestrian zone where cars and motorcycles are not permitted, either permanently or at certain times of the day.

I-SPY points: 10

Date: _____

HOUSE NUMBER

Some houses have painted tiles or signs showing their number...

I-SPY points: 15

Date: _____

HOUSE NAME

...and some houses have no number at all, just a name!

I-SPY points: 15

Date: _____

OLD STREET NAME

Street name signs are often bolted to the side of buildings. Here is an example of a new sign fixed below the original stone sign.

I-SPY points: 20

Date: _____

CHANGED STREET NAME

Look for unusual street names, especially where the name has changed. The old name often gives a clue to what was there before.

I-SPY points: 25

Date: _____

DOCTORS PARKING

Doctors may have their own parking areas provided they have the correct permit. This saves time if they need to attend emergencies.

I-SPY points: 15

Date: _____

CYCLE ROUTE

Riding a bicycle is a good way to reduce traffic congestion and is great for the environment. Here is a direction sign for a cycle route.

I-SPY points: 10

Date:

MULTIPLE SIGN

This sign has at least seven different places of interest.

I-SPY points: 5 for each or 50 for a sign of six or more on one signpost

Date:

SKIP

Builders need skips – big metal containers – to clear away rubble and rubbish from building sites.

I-SPY points: 10

Date: _____

MEN AT WORK

When you see this sign you can be sure that roadworks are ahead and sometimes traffic jams!

I-SPY points: 10

Date: _____

PUBLIC TOILET

A relief to those in need!

I-SPY points: 5

Date: _____

WALL POST BOX

Postboxes set in to walls were onc a common sight, less so today.

I-SPY points: 20

Date: _____

POST BOX

...but the red pillar box is a more familiar sight on British Streets. *When was the first post box erected in Britain?*

I-SPY points: 5
Double with answer

Date: _____

TELEPHONE BOX

Telephone boxes are gradually disappearing from British streets, as most people now have mobile phones. The old red boxes are becoming less easy to find.

I-SPY points: 15

Date: _____

LITTER BIN

In many places litter bins now have several different slots so that rubbish can be sorted and recycled more easily. Always put litter in the bins provided.

I-SPY points: 5

Date: _____

TOWN HALL

The Town Hall is usually centrally placed and is often a grand building.

I-SPY points: 10

Date: _____

GRIT BOX

Big yellow boxes, at the road side, store grit to spread on the roads in the winter to melt the ice.

I-SPY points: 10

Date: _____

NEWSPAPER BOARD

Boards outside newsagents advertise the news headlines. Take a seat and read the paper!

I-SPY points: 10

Date: _____

BENCH

You may want to take a rest from walking or shopping, what better place than a bench to rest on.

I-SPY points: 5

Date: _____

FLOWERS ON LAMPPOST

Flowers always brighten up the day!

I-SPY points: 15

Date: _____

Look Around I-SPY

FOUNTAIN

Fountains can vary from very elaborate structures to more simple water features like the one in the picture.

I-SPY points: 10

Date: _____

STATUE

Statues often commemorate important local people or events and give you a chance to learn the local history.

I-SPY points: 10

Date: _____

BICYCLES

Some university cities have a lot of bicycles and bicycle parking. Here is a row of bikes on cycle racks on the pavement.

I-SPY points: 10

Date: _____

DROPPING LITTER

This all-in-one sign tells you not to drop any litter, gum or cigarettes – or face a fine!

I-SPY points: 20

Date: _____

own centres are home to smaller shops that often only
ell one type of product, such as bread or vegetables.
upermarkets are much larger and are usually sited on
he edge of a town.

BUTCHER

For all your fresh meats.

I-SPY points: 5

Date: _____

BAKER

What beautiful smells from the
bakery in the morning.

I-SPY points: 5

Date: _____

Libraries and cafés offer shoppers a chance to have a rest while out shopping!

COFFEE SHOP/ CAFÉ

I-SPY points: 5

Date: _____

SANDWICH SHOP

Choose your favourite...

I-SPY points: 5

Date: _____

LIBRARY
I-SPY points: 10

Date:

KEY CUTTING SHOP
I-SPY points: 10

Date:

SHOE SHOP
I-SPY points: 5

Date:

CHEMISTS

I-SPY points: 10

Date: _____

CASHPOINT MACHINE

See how many cashpoint machine you can see on your high street.

I-SPY points: 5

Date: _____

ANTIQUE SHOP

I-SPY points: 10

Date: _____

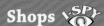

INDIAN RESTAURANT

I-SPY points: 5

Date: _____

CHINESE RESTAURANT

I-SPY points: 5

Date: _____

FISH AND CHIPS

Traditionally the most popular fast food in Britain.

I-SPY points: 5

Date: _____

CAR SHOWROOM

I-SPY points: 5

Date: _____

BOOKSHOP

I-SPY points: 5

Date: _____

FLORIST

I-SPY points: 5

Date: _____

CHARITY SHOP

Pick up a bargain.

I-SPY points: 5

Date: _____

TRADITIONAL CAFÉ

I-SPY points: 15

Date: _____

BARBERS (WITH STRIPY POLE)

Stripy barbers' poles might be a bit harder to find!

Traditionally barbers' shops have a red and white striped pole outside. Why?

I-SPY points: 15
Double with answer

Date: _____

CAKE SHOP
So much to choose from...
I-SPY points: 10
Date:

GREENGROCER
For all your fruit and vegetables.
I-SPY points: 10
Date:

SUPERMARKET
I-SPY points: 5
Date:

BIG ICE CREAM

There's nothing better than a big ice cream on a hot day!

I-SPY points: 10

Date: _____

SHOPPING TROLLEY

Shopping trolleys of one form or another are increasingly popular.

I-SPY points: 10

Date: _____

PETROL STATION

Look at all the different types of fuel.

I-SPY points: 5

Date: _____

There are a surprising number of uniforms to spot on the street – see how many you can find.

HOTEL PORTER

I-SPY points: 15

Date: _____

POSTMAN

I-SPY points: 5

Date: _____

TRAFFIC WARDEN

I-SPY points: 10

Date: _____

SUPERMARKET DELIVERY MAN

I-SPY points: 10

Date: _____

ROAD MARKER

I-SPY points: 20

Date: _____

WINDOW CLEANER

Watch out for the window cleaner's ladder!

I-SPY points: 15

Date: _____

PAINTER/ DECORATOR

I-SPY points: 10

Date: _____

BIG ISSUE SELLER

I-SPY points: 15

Date: _____

BUSKER

Buskers entertain shoppers and passers by and collect donations in a hat or box on the pavement.

I-SPY points: 15

Date: _____

CHILD IN HEELYS

nd watch out for someone
peeding towards you in heelys
the trainers with built-in wheels.

-SPY points: 10

ate:

TOWN CRIER

own criers, with their traditional
olourful outfits are sometimes
ound in older cities.

-SPY points: 25

ate:

BABY IN A BUGGY

I-SPY points: 10

Date: _____

SOMEONE CARRYING SHOPPING

How many different shopping bags can you see around you?

I-SPY points: 15

Date: _____

MOBILITY SCOOTER

Older or infirm people often use mobility scooters to get around.

I-SPY points: 15

Date: _____

Index

First published by Michelin Maps and Guides 2010 © Michelin, Proprietaires-Editeurs 2010. Michelin and the Michelin Man are registered Trademarks of Michelin. Created and produced by Horizons Publishing Limited. All rights reserved. No part of this publication may be reproduced, copied or transmitted in any form without the prior consent of the publisher. Print services by FingerPrint International Book production – fingerprint@pandora.be. The publisher gratefully acknowledges the contribution of the I-Spy team: Camilla Lovell and Jordan Watts in the production of this title. The publisher gratefully acknowledges the contribution of Judith Millidge and Ian Murray. The publisher also gratefully acknowledges the co-operation and assistance of the following who supplied pictures for this title: Britain on View, Tesco Stores Limited, Cancer Research UK, BAA-images, Kent County Council, Karel Hladky, Will Shires, Newcastle County Council, Andrew Dunn, Black Country Living Museum, unitaw, Leeds Media Store, Sally Blackmore, Peter Moore, Smartsetpix, Camilla Lovell, East Riding Media Library, Chris Parker. Other images in the public domain and used under a creative commons licence. All logos, images and designs are © the copyright holders and are used with thanks and kind permission.

Answers: P4 Pelican Crossing, pedestrian light controlled crossing, **P5** Belisha Beacon, Named after Leslie Hore-Belisha, the Minister of Transport who introduced them in 1934. **P44** Post Box, The first British pillar boxes appeared in Jersey in 1852, the first on the mainland in Carlisle in 1853. **P55** Barbers Pole, In medieval times Barbers also used to perform surgery and tooth extractions. The pole represents the red of the blood and the white of the bandages.

I-SPY
One
Token

715298

HOW TO GET YOUR I-SPY CERTIFICATE AND BADGE

Every time you score 1000 points or more in an I-Spy book, you can apply for a certificate

HERE'S WHAT TO DO, STEP BY STEP:

Certificate

- Ask an adult to check your score
- Ask his or her permission to apply for a certificate
- Apply online to www.ispymichelin.com
- Enter your name and address and the completed title
- We will send you back via e mail your certificate for the title

Badge

- Each I-Spy title has a cut out (page corner) token at the back of the book
- Collect five tokens from different I-Spy titles
- Put Second Class Stamps on two strong envelopes
- Write your own address on one envelope and put a £1 coin inside it (for protection). Fold, but do not seal the envelope, and place it inside the second envelope
- Write the following address on the second envelope, seal it carefully and post to:

I-Spy Books
Michelin Maps and Guides
Hannay House
39 Clarendon Road
Watford
WD17 1JA